20th century *Art.*

From
the
Louise
and
Walter
*Arensberg collection.*

October 20
to
December 18
1949

The *A*rt
Institute
of
Chicago

Acknowledgments:

We want to thank the following for their help in the preparation of
this catalogue: Henry Aronson, Lester B. Bridaham, William S. Lieberman,
Patrick T. Malone, Rachael Brenner, Carl O. Schniewind,
James Johnson Sweeney, Hugo Weber, Carola Giedion-Welcker,
Morton D. Zabel and the many artists and others who have supplied
further information. We owe a particularly heavy debt to Louise and
Walter Arensberg and to Marcel Duchamp for their generous
help in assembling the material for the catalogue. Without
their cooperation it would have been impossible.

Cover, typographic design and format by Paul Rand

Printed by Hillison & Etten Company, Chicago

## Introduction to the Arensberg Collection

Over a period of more than thirty years Louise and Walter Arensberg have been acquiring modern and earlier works of art, always with an eye to the deep interrelationships which exist between vastly separated epochs. Though the collection is celebrated throughout the world as one of the best integrated sources for the study of contemporary painting it is not by any means limited to the twentieth century. A large and important section of Pre-Columbian sculpture along with American Indian material, various examples of primitive art including excellent African carvings, a few early European and American paintings and a small group of Mexican *retablos* make up the remainder of the collection.

Though the Art Institute exhibition contains most of the twentieth century section there are certain omissions. In many instances prints, particularly well known etchings and lithographs which can readily be seen elsewhere, have not been included; also occasional objects, too fragile for transportation, have not been sent. The work of certain nineteenth century forerunners appears in the exhibition, specifically paintings by Cézanne, Renoir and Henri Rousseau, in each case an artist who has left his mark deeply incised on the minds of his followers.

In the Arensberg Collection may be seen in extraordinary variety the logical development of early Cubism, possibly the most important single art movement of our century. Here are many of the greatest Cubist paintings by Picasso, Braque and their lesser known contemporaries, Gleizes, Picabia, Delaunay, Jacques Villon and Metzinger ranged before us in a kind of kaleidoscopic history of those pioneer years between 1908 and 1913. The year 1912 emerges as a particularly heroic one for this movement; artist after artist carries Cubism forward to new and unsuspected developments. Significantly, many of the best known Cubist paintings of this year are in the Arensberg Collection.

Throughout, an astonishing continuity has been achieved. Certain twentieth century trends have been stressed by the collectors and others deliberately avoided. Though Cubist and Surrealist works appear in great number the purely decorative tradition and the tendency towards emotional exaggeration are usually absent. Whereas early Picasso, Braque, Gris and Léger are brilliantly represented, also Kandinsky, Klee and Miró, there is only one excellent Chagall, characteristically chosen from a year when this artist first felt the impact of Cubism. There is also but a single example of Rouault's fervid Expressionism. The only painting by Matisse, a portrait of Mlle. Yvonne Landsberg (No. 137), is one of those rare works where this artist renounces his usual color patterning in favor of a strongly stated design which was Matisse's own answer to abstraction. Most of the paintings and sculpture in the exhibition were done in France either by artists born there or by foreigners attracted to Paris through its international movement. There are certain exceptions, notably Klee, Kandinsky and Jawlensky, but the few American painters like Demuth, Sheeler and Morton Schamberg reflect more the French international tradition.

The work of two men stands out in the collection, not only for the extent to which each is represented, but because Marcel Duchamp and Constantin Brancusi are among the most original and influential of contemporary artists. Here are almost all of Duchamp's paintings and drawings; here also is the largest single group of sculpture by Brancusi. So secure is the place of Duchamp and Brancusi in the art of our century that they can serve as cornerstones of this collection — a fact reflected in two special studies on their work included in this catalogue.

The nearer this century approaches its half-way mark the clearer it becomes that our leading painters and sculptors have concerned themselves with a few main ideas. Above the battle of the "isms" certain directions are emerging which characterize the art of today.

The twentieth century artist started with a reaction against the dissolving, transient elements in Impressionism. Form in the followers of Monet and Pissarro had tended to be lost in a haze of light; without form meaning had evaporated until painting was drifting into mere surface decoration. In the works of Cézanne and Seurat, however, young artists found a restatement of earlier principles together with something new on which they could found their own contemporary vision. Both of these predecessors had disciplined Impressionism by structure, Cézanne in order to express his profound emotions before nature, Seurat to transform nature into haunting enigmatic patterns of line and space. The discovery of African and other primitive sculptures with their reduction to simple unrealistic forms coincided with the realization that both Cézanne and Seurat had stressed geometric solids. Henri Rousseau's naiveté which avoided Impressionism altogether to concentrate on a careful building up of the picture through flat planes of color suggested still another way to recapture lost elements of form.

Picasso's vigorous reaction against his own poetic and gracile early work set the stage for the new advance. Going beyond the Post-Impressionists by way of early Iberian and African carvings, he began to destroy the world of casual appearances inherited from the Renaissance, to construct a new, exciting world of free forms in liberated space. A Female Nude (No. 172) becomes the theme for drastic analysis. Reduced to planes, lines, angles and ovoids, Picasso combines these elements into a wholly original structure. The fixed viewpoint – another Renaissance concept – is replaced by a multiple viewpoint while color is limited to a few tones as befits the serious abstracting and remaking of form. The result is a wholly new dynamic of motion. As Picasso's collaborator, Braque, announced, "I do not wish to repeat an old experience. I want to create a new one."

Thus many artists working in close unison in Paris before the first world war adopted the direction suggested by these two innovators. Within the framework of such ideas artists developed their own contributions, Picabia stressing motion through an interplay of faceted and weaving shapes in Dances at the Spring (No. 160) and Catch as Catch Can (No. 161), Gleizes tending towards a monumental architecture of half-abstract elements in his Man on the Balcony (No. 90), Metzinger forcing decorative and expressive fragments into new relationships in The Bathers (No. 146). But already in certain paintings Picasso and Braque were demonstrating a new concern with another solution. Abandoning their meticulous analysis of the object, they began to turn the picture itself into an object. It became subservient to its own rules. No longer does it attempt to interpret nature through recombining and rebuilding many elements. The artist selects only a few forms and uses them to construct a work of art which exists on its own level. Picasso's Man with Violin (No. 174) is not a man with a violin. It is not even a painting of a man with a violin. It is first and foremost *a painting*. Léger's vision of the contemporary world which attempts successfully to create a picture, functioning with the precision and elegance of a machine, leads on to the ultimate stage of this tendency which is found in the austerely disciplined rectangles and lines of Mondrian.

In contrast to this direction and growing up at almost the same time is a second tendency, differing strongly from the careful analysis and rebuilding of the Cubists. Early works by Kandinsky like his Improvisations of 1912 and 1914 (Nos. 102 and 103) seem to have been arrived at spontaneously. The artist allows color and line to flow into purely emotional patterns. Here one feels the invention of form to express a psychological idea. Kandinsky's method of freely associated elements opens a whole new tradition of sensations and meanings which often appear almost primitive in their intensity. Many of the most successful works by Masson and Miró stem from this impulse. States of awareness and tension are suggested by biomorphic shapes, playing in combination with rhythmic drawing and unfettered space. Klee's varied and subtle world is delicately linked to nature but imagination and fantasy transform his idea until the painting seems to shift and change and develop before one's eyes.

Even the avowed Surrealists, men like Dali and Magritte, employ these principles of organic shape and romantic space though they clothe them in meticulous and symbolic realism. This tradition of interior meaning finds its echo in the reliefs of Arp and even in the mobiles of Calder where abstracted forms move enigmatically in an orbit of actual space. Tanguy's dream world, precise and at the same time psychologically compelled, is but another example where the artist's inner vision rather than his outer eye controls and dominates. Truly this second direction has been responsible for liberating unexpected resources in twentieth century art.

The hard-used term "abstract" means relatively little in our period of loose terminology. In the Arensberg Collection works by Braque, Gris and Léger are labeled abstract no less than totally different and far more emotional paintings by Kandinsky, Masson and Miró. Beyond this flimsy definition, what do these men and their contemporaries have in common? What simple or complex vision binds them to their period and to each other?

Throughout contemporary art there appears over and over an insistence on simultaneity, a desire to show all sides of an object, all phases of an experience at one time, the entire motion, the total psychological content in one concerted impact. Almost foretelling the continuous over-lay of modern life, artists, even early in this century, recognized the meaning of speed and its relation to transportation and communication. Traveling by fast train or car, the landscape becomes kaleidoscopic and the eye sees all aspects of the scene at once. Perspective has been changed no more by rising above the land in an airplane than by moving swiftly across it in modern conveyances, and the eye must meet these new challenges with constant inner adjustments. Equally simultaneous is the frightening speed of communication, the radio which spreads in a split second the news of the world to the entire world and newspapers which hourly roll off greased presses onto the streets.

Symbols of simultaneity are manifold; the motion picture as opposed to the still photograph, television which becomes a super-simultaneous experience, even the much discussed and little understood theory of relativity where time and space merge. Freudian psychology with its recognition of the unconscious has insisted on the immediate interlacing of past and present emotions. Repeatedly the twentieth century artist, reacting to these stimuli, has tried to force on to his canvas similar time-space relations.

As early as 1910 the Cubists were concerning themselves with this problem of simultaneity, for them a formal kind of vision where the intention was to show all sides of an object at one time. After all, they reasoned, why compete with the photographer who can reproduce in perfect detail any single aspect of a subject? Freedom is the painter's prerogative; he can show with arbitrary independence the entire object, front, back, sides, inside, top and bottom, rearranged in a new and original design. The Futurists, only a few years later, borrowed the idea and applied it not too successfully to motion. If the Cubists could show all sides of an object at once, then why not depict its continuous motion in the same way? Heretofore motion in a canvas had been achieved through suggestion, often by catching a climactic moment of rest between violent periods of movement. The Futurists — paradoxical realists — wanted to do more than suggest their theme; they wanted to depict and capture it on canvas, and this they tried to do by a series of overlapping forms which illustrated the path of the object through space.

A far more complicated art, dependent as well on simultaneity, has developed in recent years from psychoanalytic experiments. The best of so-called Surrealism is unquestionably based on a compulsive combination of subconcious experiences arranged irrationally on a single canvas in which the past, the present and intervening psychological states are superimposed. Even the tricks of *trompe l'oeil,* in no way a new idea, have been revived because of their double vision and double meaning. Later works by Picasso, where seated female figures seem to rotate in three dimensions, are but other examples of this same insistence on continuous vision. One sees all sides of the woman at the same time, not reassembled as in early Cubism, but as a total figure moving slowly around within the canvas.

In Brancusi it is the condensation of symbols which expresses simultaneity. Take The Princess (No. 13), a bronze sculpture which on first glance suggests the sensuous beauty of a woman, but on further study reveals the strong phallic symbol of the male. Thus in one figure the sculptor captures both sexes in their full union. Likewise in his many versions of abstracted bird forms he makes a concentrated statement combining motion and form in a single vision.

Duchamp-Villon's Horse (No. 82) is in similar vein a curious union of man-made machine and animal. The horse form is not entirely obliterated but it is transformed, allowing the animal and its mechanistic master to combine in one sculpture. Here the artist, well in advance of his time, envisions a robot world where man, beast and machine melt into hieratic symbols of steel contours and hard surfaces. But perhaps it is his brother, Marcel Duchamp, who carries simultaneity to its ultimate conclusion. Even in his early work he combines in one painting many different aspects of his subject, for to him no single experience can ever be isolated from its visual or psychological overtones. Like most of the great twentieth century artists he reacted to the complexities of his day and infused his work with multiple meanings.

*Katharine Kuh and Daniel Catton Rich*

# Marcel Duchamp

When Marcel Duchamp was twenty-four years old – that was in 1911 – he suddenly grew up as an artist. During that year and the following, many if not most of his important works were produced. A large proportion of these are in the Louise and Walter Arensberg Collection. For that matter, at least three quarters of his work is there.

Prior to 1911 there were certain revealing dates in Duchamp's life, dates which at least superficially may help to explain his incredible art career which was telescoped with amazing intensity into scarcely more than six years. There is his birth date, 1887, in a French town called Blainville. I believe at one point he was trained as a librarian and served as such at Sainte-Geneviève. I'm not sure that this is important, but it is interesting since his two distinguished older brothers also started in professions other than art. Duchamp-Villon, eleven years older than Marcel, was trained as a doctor, but well before his untimely death in 1918 had transformed himself into a sculptor, one of the first in the twentieth century consciously to attempt an integration of sculpture and architecture. The oldest of the three, Jacques Villon, started as a lawyer and early shifted to painting, a profession he is still successfully following in Paris today.

The year 1911 becomes important in Marcel Duchamp's life for another reason. Toward the end of that year he, along with Duchamp-Villon, formally joined the Cubists. At that time the most active members of the group were Metzinger, Gleizes, Laurencin, Delaunay, le Fauconnier and Léger. Conspicuously absent from the active group were Braque, Picasso and Gris, the three names today most readily associated with Cubism. Shortly after Duchamp and his older brother joined the movement, Juan Gris and Francis Picabia did the same.

But 1911 was memorable for Marcel Duchamp not alone because he became a member of a famous group, but because at this particular time he was destined to start an abbreviated period of concentrated art productivity. Possibly in the entire history of art no single figure has revolutionized and foretold his epoch in so short a time. Now at the end of the first half of this century we still have not caught up with him. He remains the outstanding precursor of his period.

In 1911 Duchamp produced The Sonata (No. 56), a large multiple portrait of his mother and three sisters, executed deftly in light delicate colors, its vertical design in no way obscuring the tender if cool psychological interpretation of the feminine members of his family. Only a year earlier he had painted the portrait of his father (No. 53). When much later he saw it at the Arensberg's home in Hollywood he said, "Un peu Cézannesque." This can be a key to the primary roots of his work – Cézanne, the most solid, the most cerebral, with possibly Seurat as an exception, of all late nineteenth century painters. And it is curious to know that Duchamp, during a New York interview in 1915, placed Seurat above Cézanne as the greatest scientific artist of the last century. But also in that same interview he said, "The dead should not be permitted to be so much stronger than the living." For by 1915 he had long since freed himself of the more overt influences from the past.

Only a few months earlier than the portrait of his father is a tentatively painted Head of a Woman in the Arensberg Collection, also dated 1910. This fragment, poorly articulated and immature, is the only work by Duchamp which reflects the influence of Matisse. Less than a year later, miraculously, he was to start some of his major works.

In 1911, along with The Sonata, he painted another family portrait group called Yvonne and Magdeleine Torn in Tatters (No. 57). This interpretation of two of his three sisters is notable because here a kind of complicated double vision takes place, an overtone of multiple meanings which foretells his later many-sided simultaneous compositions. Each sister is depicted twice, in her youth and in her maturity. Between the four profile heads, emerging for us with slow surprise, are interwoven empty spaces which at times are more important compositionally than the forms themselves. Recalling The Sonata in its delicate soft color is another painting of 1911 entitled Portrait (No. 58). Here ephemeral interlaced figures become five portraits of one woman, which, on second view, strangely combine to form a single voluptuous nude. Again there is a foretaste of simultaneous representation, again the first symptoms of Duchamp's later interest in experiments with *trompe l'oeil,* again his insistence on psychological content. The philosophy of simultaneity was not an isolated phenomenon for him, since the whole structure of Cubism is predicated on this idea – the ambitious desire to show all sides of an object at once. Futurism, developing at the same time in Italy, though more naive, also concerned itself with simultaneity, less in terms of form, more in terms of motion.

From 1911 also come the taut sketch (No. 59) and the unfinished painting (No. 60) of The Chess Players, a canvas where the forms are more disassociated than in earlier paintings of that year. The subject also has consuming interest for it is reputed that in the early twenties Duchamp abandoned painting for chess, a game which to this day captures his imagination and his enthusiasm. In the unfinished canvas (unfinished because it was invited to the Armory show and lack of time prevented its completion) a new technical brilliance appears. The forms, though transparent, are conceived with hard contours. Two central figures, intent on their game, dominate the group of repeated diminishing figures in the background but not the small solid chessboard arbitrarily placed in the upper center of the painting. The background figures are smaller repetitions of the two chess players who happen to be the artist's brothers. Here already Duchamp anticipated overlapping forms, a technique which he was to use so effectively in Nude Descending a Staircase.

Possibly 1911 is most famous in Duchamp's career because during the last month of that year the first drawing (No. 61) and the initial oil sketch (No. 62) for Nude Descending a Staircase were made. Duchamp himself tells us that "The idea of the Nude came from a drawing which I had made in 1911 to illustrate Jules Laforgue's poem *Encore à cet astre*. I had planned a series of illustrations of Laforgue's poems but I only completed three of them. In the drawing *Encore à cet astre* the figure is, of course, mounting the stairs. But while working on it, the idea of the Nude, or the title – I do not recall which – first came to my mind." From this fragmentary idea evolved the now celebrated Nude Descending a Staircase which was painted in 1912.

Very little has been written about Marcel Duchamp and what has been written is chiefly esoteric and private. It would seem that he is best known to intellectuals in terms of metaphysics, to the general public in terms of the over-publicized but nonetheless masterful painting, Nude Descending a Staircase. I am inclined to believe that this is in no sense his greatest canvas. The King and Queen as well as The Bride (both in the Arensberg Collection) though less well known are to my mind superior. Still the Nude is of historic importance not alone because of the public cries and newspaper nonsense which gave it front page prominence during and after the Armory show, but because it is a landmark of Cubism. Often erroneously considered Futurist, since the general idea of the painting is one of descending motion, Duchamp has vigorously denied this association. A few years ago he said, ". . . my interest in painting the Nude was closer to the Cubists' interest in decomposing forms than to the Futurists' interest in suggesting movement. . . ." Even so, I am tempted to agree with Julien Levy's statement that "As a Cubist he (Duchamp) disciplined Futurism," for in his work the boundaries between the two schools melted and met.

All four versions of the Nude are in the Arensberg Collection, the first drawing and the oil sketch mentioned above, the famous Nude Descending a Staircase, Number 2 (No. 63) which appeared in the Armory show and the lesser known Nude, Number 3 (No. 64) which was painted specially for the Arensbergs while Duchamp was in New York during 1916. Because they were unable to purchase the original Nude until the early twenties, Duchamp obligingly made for them a water color, ink, crayon and pastel version over a photographic base taken from the original. Steel blue and gray, tense and lucid, this later Nude rivals its model or, shall we say, parent, for Duchamp signed it "Marcel Duchamp (Fils)" inferring that this was the son of the earlier painting.

All during 1912 Duchamp concerned himself with problems relating to motion, to the decomposition and correlative reassembling of form, while to these structural processes he added a new element which he himself describes in this way: "I wanted to get away from the physical aspect of painting. I was much more interested in recreating ideas in painting. For me the title was very important." Consistently from the beginning he relied on the suggestive relationship of literary meaning and abstracted form. It was in this respect that he broke completely with the other Cubists and foretold Surrealism, a good four years even before the birth of Dada. Witness the fact that Duchamp is not sure whether it was the plastic idea of the Nude or its title which first started him working on the painting. Study The King and Queen Surrounded by Swift Nudes (No. 67) and you will see that this canvas, one of Duchamp's masterpieces, is a miracle of technique and idea, of form interwoven with interior content. Every possible variety of circular, rotating and diagonal motion are here introduced with the condensed color, form and power of a Masaccio. What does the painting mean? Duchamp says, "My King and Queen was a chess king and queen." In any case, the King at the right, the Queen on the left, form stable islands between which their "subjects" rush and move with an almost frightening energy. The implications are left to the observer.

An equally great painting of the same year, certainly one of the most important canvases to come from the first half of the twentieth century, is The Bride (No. 69). Executed with astounding technical mastery The Bride is a new kind of anatomical abstraction where light and form are totally integrated. Gabrielle Buffet-Picabia calls it "a complex motor running on love-gas." Here Duchamp's debt to the machine is clear, a machine which he saw in terms of our century, macabre, playful, ironic and sad. His abstracted forms are never simple statements of one idea; they suggest constant baffling and paradoxical overtones with humor always tempering terror. Contemporary artists like Yves Tanguy, Max Ernst and Matta owe much to The Bride. They, too, are interested in the strange alive-dead personal machines which Duchamp created years ago and which, both mechanistic and human, combine to make a new form of present day life. Perhaps the ingenious cartoonist, Rube Goldberg, borrowed from the same philosophy.

The Bride was painted as one of many studies for Marcel Duchamp's most important single work, The Bride Stripped Bare by Her Own Bachelors, which is better known as "the large glass." From late 1912 until 1923 much of Duchamp's painting, whether on canvas or glass, was preparation for this final work which is now in Katherine Dreier's collection in Milford, Connecticut. At the Arensberg house alone are at least nine different associated works, most important of which are The Bride, Glider and the Water Mill and the two Chocolate Grinders, though many of the lesser known sketches and plans are possibly even more interesting as evidence of how the artist developed his vast project. Take, for example, Cemetery of Uniforms and Liveries (No. 70), a kind of blueprint for the "bachelors" in the large glass, which shows how minutely Duchamp worked and with what astonishing mathematical precision. This document is also remarkable because of its insidious meaning, the implied relationship between uniforms of officialdom and the sterility of a cemetery. Of the large glass André Breton says, "Mechanistic and utterly cynical interpretation of the phenomenon of love: the passage of woman from the state of virginity to that of non-virginity taken as the theme of a fundamentally a-sentimental speculation. . . ."

Glider and the Water Mill (No. 72) in the Arensberg Collection is Duchamp's first glass and incidentally the only unbroken one now in existence. The large glass smashed into bits at one time when it was moved but since then Duchamp has laboriously fitted the small pieces together. When first he started working with glass he attempted to engrave directly on its surface, hoping to make grooves which would act as lines. For some reason or other he found that this method didn't work so he substituted flexible lead wire applied with paint and varnish. Both the large glass and Glider and the Water Mill were made this way—actually drawn in wire, an idea which Duchamp likes because it is impersonal. He preferred, as he said, "not showing the work of my own hand all the time." To him pliable wire is far less personal than a line drawn by hand with a pencil. The idea implicit in all of his glass constructions is transparency, the unification of the work of art with its surroundings by looking at and through it simultaneously. In this way, particularly in the case of Glider and the Water Mill, which is hinged and can be moved, a new vision constantly unfolds as the design on the glass is seen against different objects in the room or out of the window or in reflections cast on the surface of the glass.

Among the numerous ways Duchamp has shown himself a pioneer is in this use of transparent mediums. Experiments with light and plastics by Gabo, Pevsner and Moholy-Nagy may easily have grown out of Duchamp's "glasses" and unquestionably Calder's mobiles have been influenced by Duchamp's much earlier moving constructions, the first of which was made in 1913. A year later came the ready-mades, another revolutionary idea. Breton's definition is perhaps the best. He says that ready-mades are "manufactured objects promoted to the dignity of objects of art through the choice of the artist. . . ." As Duchamp lost faith in the old forms, as he became gradually an anti-artist, he depended more and more on the ready-made. For him the process of selection and recognition was a creative act of as important dimensions as the painting of a more traditional canvas. Here he was concerned with the act, not the result. Any object, isolated and divorced from its functional meaning, can become a ready-made, either with or without further embellishment. In a sense this acceptance of everyday objects in terms of art made possible a new attitude for the public, a fresh way of looking at one's own surroundings with both amusement and esthetic enjoyment. A telling example of a Duchamp ready-made is the painted tin advertisement, Girl with Bedstead (No. 77), which the artist changed by adding and deleting a few words and letters here and there, thus intensifying and enlarging the original meaning. Not to be overlooked is the witty play on Guillaume Apollinaire's name, for the sign advertises an enamel with a name reminiscent of the famous poet who became the accepted spokesman for the Cubists.

The ready-made belongs to Dada, a strong nihilist movement which grew out of the frustrations and disillusionments of the first world war. Jean Arp has wisely said, "Dada is senseless like nature." And in describing the whole idea Arp further wrote, "Dada objects are formed of elements found or manufactured, simple or heteroclite. The Chinese several thousand years ago, Duchamp, Picabia in the United States, Schwitters and myself during the war of 1914 were the first to invent and disseminate these games of wisdom and clairvoyance which were to cure human beings of the raging madness of genius and return them modestly to their rightful place in nature." The ready-made incorporated audience participation and removed the awesome capital "A" from art while at the same time it became the logical forerunner of the better known Surrealist *objet trouvé*.

In 1915 Duchamp came to the United States for the first time. Five years later in New York City the enigmatic Rrose Sélavy was born, a pseudonym particularly useful for signing ready-mades and for increasing anonymity. Duchamp tells us "The name evolved from a pun on French words: C'est la vie, Sélavy. Rose being the most commonplace feminine name I could think of (French taste of the period)." The double "r" in the first name, Duchamp reports, came from a painting by Picabia which incorporated the signatures of his Parisian artist friends and which Duchamp signed using two "r's" for the first time. He says, "The end of the sentence on that painting by Picabia was as follows:  pi qu'habilla rrose Sélavy

          Pi ca    bia

The "a" of "habilla" gave me the idea to continue punning: arrose (the verb "arroser" takes two "r's") and then I thought it very clever to begin a word, a name, with two "r's", like the two "l's" in Lloyd." It is impossible to over-estimate the importance of words and their multiple meaning in connection with Duchamp's work. Lists of his witty condensed puns have been collected; most are in French and highly sophisticated, for to him the actual play on words was quite as important as the closely interrelated plastic forms. If he was anti-art he was likewise reacting against the purely abstract, since his work, though often abstracted, was always related to a kind of literary idea. The titles of his paintings were not the arbitrary fabrications used by many of his followers today, but on the contrary were integral parts of his compositions and when read correctly help to explain his work. This is not always easy, for Duchamp's inventions are never on a popular or simple level.

One only needs examine the innumerable preparatory notes he made for the large glass to realize how rich and contrived were his methods. Nothing is haphazard. Every possible angle is examined, discussed and in many cases rejected by him before he puts pencil to paper or brush to canvas. In his famous *Boite,* which contains all the written and drawn records of his research on the large glass, appear many indiscriminate associative items which become almost a psychoanalysis of the work of art. Every scribbled note, every abortive sketch is a reminder of Duchamp's tireless investigation into visual possibilities. A striking example is his early discovery that light and color are interrelated as in modern neon signs, for he was convinced that both these elements grow out of their material. Since he believed that light and color are indivisible, and that light does not emanate from the surface of a material but from within, it is clear why eventually he turned to experiments with glass. But Duchamp pushed deeper in his speculations. He felt that these elements were not alone physical, that there were always corollary inner meanings; to him light from within implied more than a simple visual experience.

Duchamp's enormous discipline shows everywhere in his work. His pseudo-scientific speculations, partially symbolic, partially rational, are always connected tightly with a central idea. Toward modern science and its machinery he developed a mysterious ambivalence where his respect was cynically dissipated by humor and doubt. His whole approach is concerned with deflating the pompous tenets of our present industrialized world. He refuses to be impressed by the hierarchy of science, though, like a small boy, he constantly plays with its symbols. For him dualism was always present, the weighing of one side against the other, balance and counterbalance. Witness his preoccupation with motion and rest, with problems connected with the relativity of speed. Like Proust, his contemporary, to Duchamp nothing is as it seems. Since Leonardo no artist has been so consumed with philosophical and technological experiments. At one time he worked with photography, hoping to change the scale of objects by mechanical means and also to obtain a new kind of motion through superimposed forms, the latter a pre-stroboscopic investigation.

But there is more than technology to Duchamp's probings, there is also poetry. He became more and more concerned with the symbolism of celibacy. For him the celibate life of today's machine-bred man and woman was conceived as a constantly recurring frustration or boomerang. As with his tongue in his cheek he tried to marry technology to art, he at the same time searched for the poetic heart in our scientific instruments. An excellent case is his own description of the basic idea behind his painting, The Bride. First there is a tank filled with love essence, an essence of only timid power which is distributed by a motor to weak cylinders in direct contact with sparks from the bride's life. The result is "magnetic desire" which explodes and evaporates. The virgin, who was just arriving at the fulfillment of her desires, faints. This condensed scenario embodies the poetic eroticism in much of Duchamp's late work.

Why, we wonder, did he, perhaps the most inventive mind in twentieth century art, suddenly stop in what seems the middle of a brilliant career? Had he said all he needed to say? Was he one of the few artists who was able to stop at his prime? Or had he set himself a goal too complicated to reach? In any case, Marcel Duchamp's name and work are woven into the fabric of contemporary history. He, in but a few years, reached out and caught single-handed the most elusive facets in the art and life of our time.

*Katharine Kuh*

Note: Quoted remarks in this article have been taken from the following books and periodicals: A Complete Reversal of Art Opinions by Marcel Duchamp Iconoclast. *Arts and Decoration*, September, 1915. *The Museum of Modern Art Bulletin*, Vol. XIII, Nos. 4-5, 1946. Julien Levy, *Surrealism*, Black Sun Press, New York, 1936. *View*, Series V, No. 1, 1945. Jean Arp, *On My Way*, Wittenborn, Schultz, Inc., New York, 1948.

# Constantin Brancusi

Sculpture in the twentieth century has not always fulfilled its obligations as a major art. Warmed over archaism, techniques lifted from painting, a too-easy insistence on direct carving as the only method, these have concealed at times a lack of invention and hollowness of form. One of the few sculptors of our time to transcend such confusion is the Roumanian-born Brancusi who for forty years in Paris has been evolving a new vision in bronze, wood and stone. Brancusi's particular way of seeing may be clearly grasped in the Louise and Walter Arensberg Collection which contains fifteen of his major pieces. Here may be sensed his striking and continual effort to endow a dull art with fresh intuitions.

When Brancusi arrived in Paris in 1904 he had academic techniques at his finger tips. He had started out as an artisan in wood-working and quickly demonstrated an almost virtuoso competence in modeling. In Paris he naturally gravitated towards Rodin and studied with him. But Rodin's large romantic gesture in form and rippling light-struck surfaces could not satisfy him. Neither could Maillol's monumental sensualism based on the Greco-Roman tradition of nude goddesses restudied through the living model.

Characteristically Brancusi sought a purer, finer and tenser solution. Retaining something of Rodin's impressionist modeling he began to discipline it in terms of simplified structure. Keeping Rodin's emphasis on the emotionally-charged fragment he attempted to endow such heads as the Sleeping Muse (1908-1910) and the Prometheus (No. 6) with a feeling of totality. Restless interior emotion which in Rodin's followers degenerated into theatricalism was held in check by a stricter ovoid form. Details were reduced and the surface allowed to stretch tautly over a few planes or relax into a smooth, general roundness. Significantly in Prometheus he has chosen the theme of a mortal who defied the gods and whose punishment was to lie bound and helpless before fate. Brancusi could dispense with the figure; nothing more than the turning poise of the head and the slightest indication of expression in a few features are needed to suggest the mood of struggle and resignation. How a similar form can evoke an entirely different response is apparent in The New Born (No. 11) where Brancusi expresses the mystery and stillness of birth. The idea of nascence and becoming is found in many other oval pieces. Infinitely varied in proportion and carving, these forms rest horizontally on bases of contrasting material, seeming at times to move and float under the changing play of light. Some of these marbles, subtly shaped and exquisitely finished to the touch, return perhaps to the pre-classical tradition of the Mediterranean or to the early Chinese. Cycladic sculpture may have suggested ovalizing and reduction of detail; T'ang and pre-dynastic China, this remarkable poise of swelling and rounded forms. Such a method had little to do with the half-realistic, half-classical proportions of much contemporary European sculpture. Though it may have responded to some of the new plastic influences of the Congo under which Modigliani carved his rare heads and caryatids, it had little to do with the expressionist elongations of Lehmbruck out of Maillol.

As Brancusi advanced he took up other themes. Sometimes he tried, as in The Kiss (No. 5), to convey concentrated primitive passion. Compared with Rodin's semi-literary eroticism, The Kiss has a new barbaric power in its stone block which drives the linked figures into ever tighter embrace. It is significant that in the Arensberg Collection such pieces are happily along with Aztec stone-carvings and often seem to give off, in a more refined and pointed manner, similar sensations of weight and psychological force. In wood, which Brancusi carves simply and often savagely, leaving behind the marks of his tools, he often seems as in The Prodigal Son (No. 9) to relate to the Gothic woodcarvers of the North. In the Chimera (No. 14) he has taken the fantastic monster of Greek mythology but his rendering is highly original. Suitable to the idea of an animal made up of different beasts is this binding together of seemingly unrelated forms, some free, some geometric, where a hole takes on the mystery of an eye and two ovoids become a strange head and arching neck. The effect is disquieting and the piece at different positions seems to shift and change with the spectator. Here he has renewed some of the magic of the image-makers of Oceania but expressed the theme with his own particular humor. In the wood bases and arches and beams on which he places or frames his sculpture and where the shining or polished forms play against rough-hewn timber, he harks back to something of his own peasant tradition.

"Nude men in sculpture are not as beautiful as toads" is one of his sayings and to express many sides of his vision he has chosen the theme of some animal or bird. The marble of the Penguins (No. 8) is an early focusing on such a theme. Three heavy rounded forms fold against one another in a balance which not only echoes the original shape of the block but conveys overtones of brooding interdependence and love. It would be a mistake to compare such sculpture to the abstract intentions of Cubism. Brancusi has always refused to ally himself with the Cubists. If like them he has sought a pure form it is only to liberate a pure emotion. "Simplicity," he writes, "is not an end in art but one arrives at simplicity in spite of oneself by approaching the real sense of things."

Nowhere is such a truth more apparent than in his lifelong search for a perfect form for the Bird in Space, two versions of which, one in marble (No. 19) and one in polished bronze (No. 15) are in the Arensberg Collection. While an earlier marble Bird (No. 7) suggests through its elegantly swelling and tapering design a bird at alert rest, Brancusi in his treatment of flight has entered another realm of meaning. This was the piece in polished bronze which brought the sculptor sensational fame in 1926 when the United States Customs challenged its right to be admitted free of duty. A farcical trial resulted which became as celebrated as the Whistler-Ruskin suit. Brancusi heard his work described as a stovepipe or a piece of dutiable metal tubing. But artists, critics and writers sprang to his defense and he eventually won his case.

Today it is hard to see how even the art-blind of 1926 could have ignored the sensations of dazzling flight and speed which are the very essence of the piece. Over the years Brancusi has concentrated on removing every extraneous touch which does not contribute to the releasing of his vision. Sometimes in marble, often in polished bronze which catches different reflections as one moves nearer or farther away, the Bird not only captures movement — one of the main intentions of twentieth century sculpture — but creates, as its title, Bird in Space, suggests, an intense spatial aura in which the form lifts and soars. Here Brancusi has found more than a single bird symbol; he has expressed something of the new visual and space world of the airplane. That this invention has influenced certain vulgarities of streamlining and has often been confused by superficial critics with the non-artistic purposes of the machine can hardly be held against him.

The longer he worked the more Brancusi eliminated the occasional distracting note of decorative elegance which at times crept into his art. If the sharp portrait of Mlle. Pogany (No. 21) seems over-stylized today, The Princess (No. 13) with its thrust and balance of heavy sensual forms escapes its period. Brancusi's developed sculpture makes frank use of life symbols. In The Kiss he was satisfied to treat an erotic subject more obviously but The Princess relies on basic natural forms which have been heightened to express a new excitement. The Torso of a Young Man (No. 17), in wood, springs from a similar use of masculine symbols of strength and dominance. In one of the many versions of The Fish (No. 18) Brancusi has placed the marble over a reflecting pool of mirror. The sensitive silhouette seems to cut through water. One may observe the most minute gradations in carving which swell or diminish the thin marble walls of the fish shape. A fastidious workman in any material, Brancusi never uses plaster models in advance or employs assistants to rough-out his ideas. Slowly chip by chip the form is discovered, its success resulting from a tension between an inner, organic force pressing outward against a taut contour. Since this contour is constantly unfolding in three dimensions his art freely escapes the dead and engraved quality of much contemporary sculpture. Though he agrees that direct carving is "the true approach to sculpture" he warns that it is the worst possible method for "those who don't know how to get there." And thoughtfully he adds "direct carving or indirect, it really doesn't matter. It's the thing made which counts."

Sculpture for the Blind (No. 20) sums up much that the sculptor has been seeking. From the Sleeping Muse through Prometheus and The New Born the vision has become clearer, more compressed. The slumbering, dreaming intensity which plays so important a part in his sculpture has nowhere been expressed with more deceptive simplicity. Even the polish of the marble has a perfection which if it had been pushed a step further might have destroyed the unity between inner and outer feeling. Such a piece, in spite of its title, was probably not meant to be touched. Rather it was intended to give off heightened tactile sensations. It must concentrate on producing harmony in the spectator through sensuous control of both form and surface. So greatly does Brancusi's sculpture depend on exact finish that one may wonder how time will deal with it. How much will remain when his polished bronzes grow dim and his marbles lose their delicacy of surface?

The best of Brancusi's sculpture bears out the sculptor's desire which is to arrive at a significant meaning by finding a perfect form. He insists—as did Michelangelo—that sculpture consists in liberating from the material a form which the artist already possesses within himself. This stress on Platonic essences has been restated in our day by Croce and in Brancusi's case is confirmed by his study not only of distant Oriental epochs but through an almost mystic identification with certain Tibetan philosophers. His desire for clarity does not spring so much from the passionate humanism of the classical Greeks as from an Eastern conception of nature, refined by cosmopolitan Paris. It is notable that in a world of struggle and death Brancusi insists on exploring themes of passionate love and birth. There is something pagan and ecstatic in his unconcealed emphasis on procreation. Motives which in other hands might grow dully phallic are here transmuted and these sculptures, so like and still so unlike nature, are best imagined in an atmosphere of sun and wind and simple things.

Working with materials as a sculptor must, Brancusi declares himself an anti-materialist. This paradox has worried some of his admirers who see him committing a modern heresy in employing wood, bronze and stone for the same motif. For them Brancusi has two answers; first that vision always transcends material. Only through experimenting with many variations can he find the perfect form. Second that in each new material delicate and fresh adjustments are apprehended. As an artist and as a man Brancusi remains simple, profound and curiously untouched by fashion or circumstance. He has treated but few themes. There have been no striking reversals or sudden failures in his art. Over the years it has simply deepened in meaning and grown consistently out from a single core. His mark has been present in the work of younger men like Arp, Henry Moore and Noguchi but Brancusi leaves no school. Today he dreams of a sculpture which relates to modern architecture not by imitating architectural tricks and devices but by setting it in the freer, opener spaces of modern building. In this environment sculpture can return to its historic role, that of embodying human aspirations in forms which are, at the same time, highly personal and grandly universal.

*Daniel Catton Rich*

Note: Quotations from Brancusi are taken from *This Quarter,* Vol. I, No. 1, 1925, p. 236. Many of the above facts are to be found in an excellent recent article on the sculptor by C. Giedion-Welcker in *Werk,* Vol. 35, No. 10, October, 1948, pp. 321 ff.

*Catalogue*  Measurements, in inches, are given in the following order: height, width and, in the case of sculpture, depth. All water color and drawing mediums are on white paper unless otherwise noted. Oil signifies oil on canvas. Water colors have been measured to the mat openings; when mounted the exact size of the paper is given. Plate mark measurements are used for etchings and drypoints; composition measurements for all lithographs. When the artist has signed and dated his work it is so indicated; otherwise dates have been procured elsewhere. Asterisks indicate works not included in the exhibition.

## ARA (Benjamin J. Kosich).
*Lives in California.*

1 Mother, Standing Figure and Child. *Oil on board, 20¼ x 12. Signed: ARA (and on the back signed and inscribed: Benjamin Dusanovich Kosich, ARA 1935 Boom Boom Barabas).*

## Archipenko, Alexander.
*Born Kiev, U.S.S.R., 1887. Worked in Paris and has lived in the United States since 1923.*

2 The Bather. *Painted relief, wood, paper and metal, 19½ x 11. Signed and dated: A Archipenko 1915.*
*This technique is called sculpto-painting by the artist.*

## Arp, Jean.
*Born Strasbourg, France, 1887. Has lived in Switzerland and France.*

3 Constellation. *Painted wood relief, 27½ x 33½ (with frame). Unsigned. 1932-1933.*

## Bouché, Louis.
*Born New York City, 1896.*

4 Lola. *Oil, 26 x 20. Unsigned. 1918 or 1919.*

## Brancusi, Constantin.
*Born Craiova, Roumania, 1876. Came to Paris in 1904 where he still lives.*

5 The Kiss. *Stone, 22¾ x 13 x 9¾. Unsigned. 1908.*
6 Prometheus. *Marble, approximately 4½ x 7 x 5. Unsigned. 1911.*
7 Bird. *Marble on marble base, 30 x 7 x 7½ (with base). Unsigned. About 1913 or 1914.*
8 Penguins. *Marble, 26 x 21 x 12½. Unsigned. 1914.*

*There is an earlier version also in marble with only two penguins.*

9 The Prodigal Son (L'Enfant Prodigue). *Wood on stone base, 29⅝ x 8½ x 8¾ (with base). Unsigned. 1914.*
10 Study for The New Born. *Pencil and wash on brown paper, 14¾x21¾ (sight measurement). Signed: C. Brancusi. About 1910-1915.*
11 The New Born (Le Nouveau Né). *Marble, approximately 6 x 9 x 5½. Unsigned. 1915.*
12 Study for The Princess. *Pencil and crayon, 16⅞ x 10⅜. Signed: C. Brancusi. About 1913-1915.*
13 The Princess. *Polished bronze on stone base, 29 x 17 x 7¾ (with base). Unsigned. 1916. Alternate titles: Madame Bonaparte, Madame P.D.K.*
14 Chimera. *Wood on wood base, 59¾ x 9½ x 9½ (with base). Unsigned. 1918.*
15 Bird in Space. *Polished bronze on marble base, 56¾ x 6 x 6 (with base). Unsigned. About 1920-1924.*
16 The Blond Negress (La Négresse Blonde). *Marble on marble base, 25½ x 8⅝ x 8⅝ (with base). Unsigned. About 1920-1925.*
17 Torso of a Young Man. *Wood on stone base, 26 x 12¼ x 7⅛ (with base). Unsigned. 1922.*
18 The Fish. *Marble on round mirror mounted on carved wood pedestal, 29¾ x 17 x 17. Unsigned. 1922.*
* 19 Yellow Bird. *Marble on marble base mounted on cement and carved wood pedestal, 50½ x 16 x 16 (with base). About 1922-1924.*
20 Sculpture for the Blind (Sculpture pour Aveugles). *Marble, approximately 6 x 12 x 7. Unsigned. 1924.*
21 Mlle. Pogany. *Marble on stone base mounted on wood pedestal, 27½ x 8¾ x 11 (with base). Unsigned. About 1928-1929.*
*This sculpture was made for Mr. and Mrs. Arensberg.*
* 22 Arch. *Wood.*
* 23 Bench. *Wood.*

## Braque, Georges.
*Born Argenteuil, France, 1882.*

24 Still Life (with the word Fox). *Drypoint, 21½ x 14⅞. Signed: G. Braque. No. 20. 1912.*
*One of Braque's earliest prints, published by Kahnweiler. Fox was the name of a Paris bar.*
25 Composition (with the word Paris). *Drypoint, 7¾ x 10¾. Unsigned. About 1912.*

26 Still Life (with the word Vin). *Collage of pencil, paper and wash on paper, 23 x 17¼. Unsigned. 1912-1913.*

27 Still Life (oval). *Collage of oil, pencil, gouache, charcoal and paper on canvas, 14 x 11. Unsigned. 1912-1913.*

28 Musical Forms (with the words Fête and Journ). *Oil and pencil on canvas, 36½ x 23½. Unsigned. About 1912-1913.*

29 Still Life. *Collage of charcoal, paper and crayon on paper, 24½ x 18¼. Unsigned. About 1912-1913.*

30 Musical Forms. *Collage of paper, corrugated cardboard and crayon on paper, 30½ x 37½. Unsigned. 1913.*

31a Still Life. *Collage of newspaper, paper, gouache, oil and charcoal on canvas, 52 x 29½. Signed and dated: G. Braque 18. 1918.*

31b The Table. *Oil, 52 x 29½. Unsigned. 1918. The above (31a and 31b) are front and back of a single canvas.*

32 Violin and Pipe. *Oil, 16¾ x 36¼. Signed on back: G Braque. 1920-1921. Alternate title: Polka.*

## Burliuk, David.
*Born Kharkov, U.S.S.R., 1882. Has lived in the United States since 1922.*

33 The Refugees. *Oil, 11 x 11. Signed: Burliuk. 1942.*

34 "Hommage à Rousseau." *Water color, 10¼ x 15. Signed, inscribed and dated lower right: David Burliuk. (First sketch to the painting) 1944. Santa Monica, Cal. Inscribed lower left: Mieur Henry Rousseau in his studio in 1906. An imaginary scene which shows Rousseau painting the Merry Jesters (No. 193 in the Arensberg Collection).*

## Calder, Alexander.
*Born Philadelphia, 1898.*

35 Mobile. *Iron, polychrome glass and string, 49 x 41¾. Unsigned. 1934.*

## Cézanne, Paul.
*Born Aix-en-Provence, France, 1839. Died Aix-en-Provence, 1906.*

36 Still Life with Apples. *Oil, 10¼ x 12¾. Unsigned. 1880-1885.*

37 Landscape with Trees. *Water color, 11½ x 18. Unsigned. 1890-1894.*

38 Group of Bathers. *Oil, 8¼ x 12¼. Unsigned. 1892-1894.*

39 Landscape. *Pencil and water color, 12 x 18½. Unsigned. 1895-1900.*

## Chagall, Marc.
*Born Vitebsk, U.S.S.R., 1889. Has worked chiefly in Paris, occasionally in the United States.*

40 Half-Past Three. *Oil, 77½ x 57¼. Signed and dated: Chagall Paris 1911. Alternate title: The Poet. This painting was given its enigmatic title, Half-Past Three, by the French poet, Blaise Cendrars, a great friend of Chagall.*

## Chirico, Giorgio de.
*Born Volo, Greece, 1888. Has worked in Paris, Florence and Rome.*

41 The Soothsayer's Recompense. *Oil, 53 x 71. Signed and dated: Giorgio de Chirico M.C.M. XIII. 1913. The French title is written on the back of the frame: La Récompense du Devin.*

42 The Poet and His Muse (Le Poète et sa Muse). *Oil, 35½ x 29. Signed and dated: G. de Chirico 21. 1921.*

## Covert, John R.
*Born Pittsburgh, 1882. Studied in Munich and Paris.*

43 Hydro cell. *Oil on cardboard, 25½ x 23¾. Inscribed lower right: Hydro cell. Signed and dated on back: Hydro cell John R. Covert N.Y.C. 1918.*

## Dali, Salvador.
*Born Figueras, Spain, 1904. Worked for many years in Paris. Now lives in the United States.*

44 Agnostic Symbol (Symbole Agnostique). *Oil, 21½ x 25½. Signed and dated: gala salvador Dali 32. 1932.*

45 Soft Construction with Boiled Beans; Premonition of Civil War. *Oil, 39x39. Unsigned. 1936.*

## Delaunay, Robert.
*Born Paris, 1885. Died South of France, 1941.*

46 St. Severin. *Oil, 38 x 27¾. Signed and dated: r. delaunay 1909.*

47 Eiffel Tower. *Oil, 51½ x 12½. Signed: R. Delaunay. About 1920-1924. Brightly colored disks are painted on the back of this canvas.*

## Demuth, Charles.

*Born Lancaster, Pennsylvania, 1883. Died Lancaster, 1935.*

48 Bermuda. *Water color and pencil, 9¾ x 13. Signed and dated: C. Demuth, 1917.*

49 Gloucester. *Water color and pencil, 23⅞ x 20. Signed and dated: C. Demuth, 1920, Lancaster, Pa.*


## Derain, André.

*Born Chatou, France, 1880.*

50 Nude. *Water color, 10¼ x 4⅜. Unsigned. About 1906-1907.*

51 Woman. *Oil, 24 x 18¼. Unsigned. About 1908-1910.*
*Alternate title: Woman Half-Length.*


## Duchamp, Marcel.

*Born Blainville, France, 1887. Has lived in the United States since 1942.*

* 52 Head of Woman. *Oil, 24 x 19⅝. Signed and dated: Duchamp 10-1910.*

53 The Artist's Father. *Oil, 36 x 28½. Signed and dated: Marcel Duchamp 10. 1910.*

54 Two Seated Figures. *Oil, 36 x 28½. Signed and dated: Marcel Duchamp 11. 1911.*

55 The Bush (Le Buisson). *Oil, 50½ x 36½. Signed and dated: Marcel Duchamp 11. 1911.*

56 The Sonata (La Sonate). *Oil, 57 x 44½. Signed and dated: Marcel Duchamp 11. 1911.*

57 Yvonne and Magdeleine Torn in Tatters (Yvonne et Magdeleine Déchiquetées). *Oil, 23½ x 28¾. Signed and dated: Dchp Sept 11. 1911.*

58 Portrait. *Oil, 57¼ x 44⅝. Signed and dated: Marcel Duchamp 11. 1911.*

59 Study for The Chess Players. *Charcoal and ink, 13 x 15⅜. Signed and dated: Marcel Duchamp 11. 1911.*

60 The Chess Players (Joueurs d'Echecs). *Oil, 39¼ x 39¼. Signed and dated: Marcel Duchamp 11. 1911.*

61 Study for Nude Descending a Staircase. *Pencil, 9⅝ x 6. Signed, dated and inscribed: Marcel Duchamp 12 Encore à cet astre Jules Laforgue. 1911.*
*Though this drawing is dated 1912 Duchamp now thinks that it was made in November, 1911, and probably signed and dated later. He signed and inscribed this drawing a second time as follows: à Monsieur F. C. Torrey très cordialement, Marcel Duchamp. 13.*

62. Nude Descending a Staircase, Number 1. *Oil on cardboard, 37¾ x 23½. Signed and dated: Marcel Duchamp 11 Nu Descendant un Escalier. 1911.*

63 Nude Descending a Staircase, Number 2. *Oil, 58⅜ x 35⅜. Signed and dated: Marcel Duchamp 12 Nu Descendant un Escalier. 1912. First sent to the exhibition of the Indépendents in Paris during February, 1912, but removed by Duchamp before the opening because of "antipathetic feelings" on the part of other exhibiting artists. The Cubists felt he was distorting Cubism. The painting was finally first publicly shown in Paris during October, 1912, at the Section d'Or.*

64 Nude Descending a Staircase, Number 3. *Water color, ink, crayon and pastel over photographic base, 58½ x 36. Signed and dated: Marcel Duchamp (Fils) 1912 1916 Nu Descendant un Escalier. 1916.*

65 Study for The King and Queen. *Pencil, 10¾ x 15⅜. Signed and dated: Le Roi et la Reine traversés par des Nus vites Marcel Duchamp 1912.*

66 Study for The King and Queen. *Water color, 19¼ x 23. Signed and dated: Le roi et la reine traversés par des nus en vitesse. Marcel Duchamp 12. 1912.*

67 The King and Queen Surrounded by Swift Nudes. *Oil, 45¼ x 50½. Signed and dated: Marcel Duchamp 12 Le Roi et La Reine entourés de Nus Vites. 1912.*

68 Study for The Virgin. *Water color, 15¾ x 10⅛. Signed and dated: Vierge Marcel Duchamp 12. 1912.*

69 The Bride. *Oil, 34¾ x 21½. Signed and dated: Mariée Marcel Duchamp August 12. 1912.*

70 Cemetery of Uniforms and Liveries. *Pencil, 12⅜ x 15¾. Signed and dated: Marcel Duchamp 13. 1913. Inscribed lower center: 1ère Esquisse du: Cimetière des Uniformes et livrées. A pattern or plan for the group of "bachelors" in the large glass.*

71 Boxing Match. *Pencil and crayon, 16½ x 12⅜. Signed and dated: Marcel Duchamp, 1913. A diagram drawing for the large glass. This was never used.*

* 72 Glider and the Water Mill. *Glass and lead wire, 59½ x 32½. Signed and dated on back: Glissière contenant un Moulin à Eau (en métaux voisins) appartenant à Marcel Duchamp 1913-14-15.*

73 Chocolate Grinder, Number 1 (Broyeuse de Chocolat). *Oil, 24 x 25. Unsigned. 1913.*

74 Chocolate Grinder, Number 2 (Broyeuse de Chocolat). *Oil, thread and pencil, 25½ x 21¼. Unsigned. 1914.*
*Thread is attached with paint and varnish and is sewn into canvas at all intersections.*

75 Ready-made, Ball of Twine (in metal frame). *5 x 5 x 5. Unsigned. 1916.*
*There are double meaning inscriptions by Duchamp on both the top and bottom of the metal frame.*

* 76 Ready-made, Comb. *1⅛ x 6½. Unsigned but dated, 1916.*
*A French inscription with the date has been printed on the back by Duchamp.*

77 Ready-made, Girl with Bedstead (Apolinère Enameled). *Painted tin advertisement, 9¼ x 13¼. Signed and dated: (from) Marcel Duchamp 1916 1917.*
*Letters and words have been altered and added by the artist on both the front and back. An interesting play on words results.*

* 78 Témoins Oculistes. *Stylus on carbon paper, 19¾ x 14¾. Signed: Rose Sélavy. 1920.*
*Study for the large glass. This is the actual carbon paper through which the design was transferred to the large glass.*

79 Ready-made, Why Not Sneeze? Rrose Sélavy. *Marble blocks in the shape of lump sugar, thermometer, wood and cuttle bone in a small bird cage, 4⅜ x 8½ x 6¼. Unsigned. 1921.*

80 Sketch for Optique de Précision. *Ink, 10¾ x 8¼. Signed and dated: Croquis pour "Optique de Précision" 1925 Marcel Duchamp.*

* 81 Bookbinding for *Ubu Roi. Leather 7⅞ x 5¼ x 1¼. 1935.*
*The binding was designed by Duchamp and made by Mary Reynolds.*

## Duchamp-Villon, Raymond.
*Born Damville, France, 1876. Died Cannes, France, 1918.*

82 Head of a Horse (Tête de Cheval). *Bronze on wood base, 23¼ x 19¾ x 17 (with base). Unsigned. 1914.*
*Three casts were made, this one, another in bronze and a third in lead.*

* 83 Portrait of Professor Gosset. *Original plaster model, 4 x 3¼ x 3½. Unsigned. 1917.*
*Has been cast in bronze.*

## Ernst, Max.
*Born Brühl, Germany, 1891. Lived in France from 1922 until 1941 when he came to the United States where he now lives.*

84 The Forest (La Forêt). *Oil, 28½ x 19¾. Signed: Max Ernst. 1923.*

85 Flower. *Oil, 25⅜ x 21. Signed: max ernst. 1928.*

86 Garden Plane Trap (Jardin Gobe-Avions). *Oil, 24 x 29½. Signed: Max Ernst 34-25. 1935.*

## Feininger, Lyonel.
*Born New York City, 1871. Worked for many years in Germany. Has lived in New York since 1937.*

87 Umpferstedt II. *Oil, 39½ x 31½. Signed: Feininger. 1914.*
*Umpferstedt is a town in Thuringia, Germany.*

## Fresnaye, Roger de la.
*Born Le Mans, France, 1885. Died Grasse, France, 1925.*

88 Nude. *Oil on board, 50½ x 22½. Signed and dated: La Fresnaye Mai 1911.*

89 Landscape. *Oil, 19 x 24. Signed and dated: R. A de la Fresnaye 12. 1912.*

## Gleizes, Albert.
*Born Paris, 1881.*

90 Man on Balcony. *Oil, 77 x 45½. Signed and dated: Albert Gleizes 12. 1912.*

91 Study for Woman at the Piano. *Water color. 10½ x 8⅛. Unsigned. About 1913.*

92 Woman at the Piano. *Oil, 57½ x 44¾. Signed and dated: Albert Gleizes 14. 1914.*

## Gris, Juan.
*Born Madrid, Spain, 1887. Died Boulange, France, 1927. Worked mainly in France.*

93 The Man in the Café (L'Homme au Café). *Oil, 50½ x 34½. Signed: Juan Gris. 1912.*
*Alternate title: The Man at the Café Table.*

94 La Place Ravignan. *Oil, 46 x 35. Signed and dated: Juan Gris 1915.*
*Alternate title: Still Life before an Open Window.*

95 The Lamp. *Oil, 32 x 25½. Signed and dated on back: Juan Gris 3-16 4e. 1916.*

96 The Open Window (La Fenêtre Ouverte). *Oil on board, 39½ x 29. Signed and dated: Juan Gris 2 1917.*

97 The Chessboard (L'Echiquier). *Oil on board, 28½ x 39. Signed and dated: Juan Gris 6-17. 1917.*

## Hélion, Jean.

*Born Couterne, France, 1904. Lived in the United States. Now back in France.*

98 Red Tensions (Tensions Rouges). *Oil, 23½ x 28½. Signed and dated on back: jean Hélion painted in Virginia 1933.*

## Jawlensky, Alexey.

*Born Twer, U.S.S.R., 1867. Died Wiesbaden, Germany, 1941. Worked chiefly in Munich and Wiesbaden.*

99 Portrait. *Oil on board, 21¼ x 19½. Signed: A. Jawlensky (and signed and dated on back) N. 6. A. Jawlensky 1912.*

100 Earth (Erde). *Oil on board, 27 x 20. Signed: Jawlensky. 1913.*
*Painted on both sides but scratched out with pencil on the back.*

101 Night (Nacht). *Oil on board, 20½ x 16½. Signed and dated: A. J. 1938.*

## Kandinsky, Wassily.

*Born Moscow, U.S.S.R., 1866. Died Paris, 1944. Painted for many years in Germany.*

102 Improvisation. *Oil, 41½ x 37½. Signed and dated: Kandinsky 1912.*

103 Improvisation. *Oil, 31 x 39¾. Signed and dated: Kandinsky 1914.*

104 Circles in Circle. *Oil, 39 x 38. Signed and dated: K 23. 1923.*

105 Landscape. *Water color, 18⅞ x 13¼. Signed and dated: K 24. 1924.*

106 Geometrical Forms. *Water color, 19 x 11⅛. Signed and dated: K 28. 1928.*

107 Fish Form. *Water color, 12⅝ x 19⅜. Signed and dated: K 28. 1928.*

108 Isolated Objects. *Water color, 19⅞ x 15. Signed and dated: K 34. 1934.*

## Klee, Paul.

*Born Berne, Switzerland, 1879. Died near Berne, 1940. Painted in Germany and Switzerland.*

109 City of Towers. *Oil on board, 12¾ x 14. Signed and dated: Klee 1916 40. Dated and inscribed on both the back and the frame: 1916. 40 Stadt der Türme.*

110 The Quenched Light. *Lithograph, 6 x 5⅛. Signed lower right pencil: Klee. Signed and dated: Klee Ausloeschendes Licht 1919, 176.*

111 Goldfish Wife. *Water color, 13¾ x 20¼. Signed: Klee. Dated and entitled on mat: 1921/93 Goldfisch Weib.*
*Alternate title: Female Goldfish.*

112 Composition. *Color lithograph, 12½ x 9. Signed and dated: Klee 1921 123.*

113 The Queen of Hearts (Hertzkoenigin). *Lithograph, 10 x 6¾. Unsigned. Dated and numbered: 1921 30 70/100.*

114 Steam Boat for Lugano. *Lithograph, 11 x 15. Signed and dated: K 1922.*

115 Tightrope Walker. *Color lithograph, 17 x 10½. Signed and dated: Klee 1923 38 Seiltänzer.*

116 Jörg. *Water color and oil on paper, 9¼ x 11¼. Signed and dated: Klee nach einer alten Bauern malerei 1924, 141. Entitled upper left: Jörg.*

117 Fish Magic. *Oil and water color on board, 30¼ x 38¾. Signed and dated: Klee 1925 R. 5. Signed and dated on back: 1925 R 5 Fischzauber Klee.*

118 Animal Terror. *Oil and gesso on canvas, 13⅞ x 19. Signed and dated: Klee 1926. U. 4. Signed and dated on back of stretcher: 1926 U 4 Der Tierschreck Klee.*

119 Demon as Pirate (Dämon als Pirat). *Water color, 11½ x 17. Signed and dated: Klee 1926.*

120 Village Carnival (Dorf Karnival). *Oil on board, 21½ x 17¼. Signed and dated: Klee 1926 D 5.*

121 Journey in Corsica. *Water color, 12⅛ x 18. Signed: Klee. Dated and entitled on mat: 1927 H. 9. Reise auf Corsica.*

122 Heavenly and Earthly Time. *Water color, 9½ x 12. Signed: Klee. Dated and entitled on mat: 1927 No 5 Kosmische und Irdische Zeit.*

123 Prestidigitator. *Oil on board, 19½ x 16½. Signed and dated: Klee 1927 Omega 7. Signed and dated on back of stretcher: 1927 Omega 7 Zauberkunststück Klee.*

124 Little Town Houses with Gardens. *Water color, 11½ x 18. Signed: Klee. Dated and entitled on mat: 1928. 0.2. Kleine Gartenstadt-Häuser.*

125 Not Ending. *Etching, 7 x 5⅜. Signed and dated: Klee 1930 K 10.*

126 Glance of a Landscape (Blick einer Landschaft). *Water color and stipple, 11¾ x 18. Signed: Klee.*

127 But the Red Roof (Aber das Rothe Dach). *Oil, 23½ x 35¾. Signed: Klee.*

## Kupka, Frank.

*Born Opocno, Czechoslovakia, 1871. Has worked chiefly in Vienna and France, where he now lives.*

128 Fugue in Two Colors. *Oil,* 39½ x 28¾. *Signed: Kupka. 1912.*

### Lebduska, Lawrence.
*Born Baltimore, 1894.*
129 White Belted Cattle. *Oil,* 24 x 30. *Signed and dated: Lebduska 37. 1937.*

### Léger, Fernand.
*Born Argentan, France, 1881. Lives in Paris but has spent some time in the United States.*
130 Contrast of Forms (Contraste de Formes). *Oil,* 51¼ x 38¼. *Unsigned. 1912 or 1913.*
131 The City. *Oil,* 51 x 38. *Signed: F. Leger. 1918-1919.*
132 Typographer, Final State (Le Typographe, Etat Définitif). *Oil,* 51 x 38. *Signed: F. Leger. 1919.*
133 Figure of a Man. *Oil,* 25½ x 19½. *Signed and dated: F Leger 20. 1920.*

### Magritte, René.
*Born Belgium, 1898. Has worked in Paris but now lives in Brussels.*
134 The Six Elements (Les Six Eléments). *Oil,* 28¾ x 39¼. *Signed: Magritte. 1928.*

### Marcoussis, Louis.
*Born Warsaw, Poland, 1883. Died France, 1941. Worked mainly in Paris.*
135 Portrait of Guillaume Apollinaire. *Etching,* 19½ x 11. *Signed: Louis Marcoussis 3/x. 1919.*
*A posthumous portrait.*

### Masson, André.
*Born Balagny (Oise), France, 1896. Lived in the United States from 1941 to 1946. Now works in France.*
136 Animal Caught in a Trap (Animal Pris au Piège). *Crayon on canvas,* 18 x 21½. *Signed on back: André Masson. 1929.*

### Matisse, Henri.
*Born Le Cateau, France, 1869.*
137 Mlle. Yvonne Landsberg. *Oil,* 58 x 38. *Signed and dated: Henri-Matisse 1914.*
138 Still Life. *Pencil,* 19⅝ x 21¾. *Signed and dated: Henri-Matisse 1915.*

### Mérida, Carlos.
*Born Quetzaltenango, Guatemala, 1893. Lives in Mexico City.*
139 Clay Figurines. *Water color,* 12¼ x 11¼ *Signed and dated: Carlos Merida 1931. Alternate title: Three Dancing Figures.*
140 The Window. *Water color,* 15 x 10. *Signed and dated: Carlos Merida 1933.*
141 Deer Dance. *Oil,* 24 x 20⅛. *Signed and dated: Carlos Merida 1935.*

### Merrild, Knud.
*Born Jutland, Denmark, 1894. Lives in Los Angeles.*
142 Portrait of D. H. Lawrence. *Gesso-wax,* 10½ x 8½. *Signed: Knud Merrild. 1933 or 1934. The portrait was made from a drawing done in 1923 when D. H. Lawrence was in Los Angeles.*
143 Arrowhead. *Gesso-wax,* 9¾ x 7⅞. *Signed: Knud Merrild. 1936.*

### Metzinger, Jean.
*Born Nantes, France, 1883.*
144 Landscape with Roofs. *Oil on board,* 16¼ x 13. *Signed: Metzinger. About 1910.*
145 Tea Time (Le Goûter). *Oil on board,* 29½ x 27½. *Signed and dated: J. Metzinger 1911. Alternate titles: Mona Lisa with a Teaspoon (Joconde à la Cuiller) or Woman with Teaspoon.*
146 The Bathers (Les Baigneuses). *Oil,* 58½ x 42. *Signed: Metzinger. 1913.*

### Miró, Joan.
*Born Barcelona, Spain, 1893. Works in Paris.*
147 The Hermitage (L'Ermitage). *Oil,* 45 x 57½. *Signed and dated: Miró 1924.*
148 Man and Woman. *Oil,* 39 x 31¾. *Signed and dated: Miró 1925.*
149 Nude. *Oil,* 36 x 29. *Signed and dated: Miró 1926.*
150 Man, Woman and Child. *Oil,* 35 x 45½. *Signed and dated: Miró 2-31. 1931.*
151 Torso. *Gouache and water color,* 17½ x 24. *Unsigned. About 1931.*
152 Figure. *Pastel,* 41¾ x 27⅝. *Unsigned. About 1934.*
153 Four Figures. *India ink and pastel,* 18½ x 24½. *Unsigned. About 1934.*
154 The Lovers (Les Amants). *Pastel,* 41¾ x 27⅝. *Unsigned. 1934.*

155 Person in the Presence of Nature (Personnage devant la Nature). *Gouache on cardboard, 29½ x 41½. Unsigned. 1935.*

## Modigliani, Amedeo.
*Born Livorno, Italy, 1884. Died Paris, 1920. Worked in Italy and Paris.*
156 Caryatid. *Crayon, 29⅛ x 23¼. Unsigned. About 1917.*

## Mondrian, Piet.
*Born Amersfoort, Holland, 1872. Died New York City, 1944. Worked in Amsterdam and Paris before coming to the United States during the second world war.*
157 Composition in Black and Gray. *Oil, 33 x 33. Signed and dated: P M 19. 1919.*
158 Composition. *Oil, 28½ x 26. Signed and dated: P M 36. 1936.*

## Montenegro, Roberto.
*Born Guadalajara, Mexico, 1885.*
159 The Double. *Oil on board, 26¼ x 20. Signed: Montenegro. 1938.*

## Picabia, Francis.
*Born Paris, 1879.*
160 Dances at the Spring. *Oil, 47¼ x 47¼. Signed and dated: Picabia 1912. Entitled upper right: Danses à la Source.*
161 Catch as Catch Can. *Oil, 39¼ x 32. Entitled upper left: Catch as Catch Can. Inscribed and dated lower center:* EDTAONISL *1913. Signed and dated on back: Picabia 1913.* EDTAONISL *is a word invented by the artist which he used in another canvas of the same period with the word Ecclesiastique.*
162 Physical Culture (Culture Physique). *Oil, 35⅛ x 45¾. Unsigned. About 1913 or 1914.*

## Picasso, Pablo.
*Born Malaga, Spain, 1881. Lives in France.*
163 Old Woman. *Oil on board, 26½ x 20½. Signed: Picasso. 1901-1903. Alternate titles: Head of Old Woman, The Hag or Woman with Gloves.*
164 Sea Shore. *Pencil, 4⅜ x 6½. Signed: Picasso. About 1905.*
165a Female Figure. *Ink, 6½ x 4. Signed: Picasso. About 1905-1906.*
165b Female Figure with Hand. *Pencil, 6½ x 4. Unsigned. About 1905-1906.*

*The above (165a and 165b) are front and back of a single sheet.*
166 Head. *Ink, 12¼ x 8⅞. Signed: Picasso. 1906.*
167 Woman Seated and Woman Standing. *Charcoal, 24¼ x 18½. Signed: Picasso. 1906.*
168 Landscape. *Gouache, 18½ x 24½. Unsigned. 1907-1908.*
169 Seated Nude Woman. *Oil, 45¾ x 35. Signed: Picasso. 1908.*
170 Men. *Gouache, 24½x18⅝. Signed: Picasso. 1908. Alternate titles: Nude Man Seated or Three Personages.*
171 Two Nude Figures. *Drypoint, 5⅛ x 4¼. Signed: Picasso. 1909.*
172 Female Nude. *Oil, 38½ x 30¼. Unsigned. 1910.*
173 Violin. *Charcoal, 18½ x 12⅜. Unsigned. About 1910-1912.*
174 Man with Violin. *Oil, 39 x 28½. Unsigned. 1911-1912.*
175 Man with Guitar. *Oil, 51¼ x 35. Unsigned. 1912-1913.*
176 Still Life with Bottle. *Drypoint, 19¾ x 12. Signed: Picasso. 1912. The words Vie and Marc appear in the composition.*
177 Violin and Guitar (oval). *Collage of pencil, appliquéd plaster, oil and material painted to simulate wood on canvas, 36¼ x 25¼. Unsigned. 1912.*
178 Three Nudes on Shore. *Pencil on tan paper, 9¾ x 16⅜. Signed and dated: Picasso 23-6-20. 1920.*
179 Still Life. *Pastel, 41 x 29¼. Signed and dated: Picasso 10-4-21. 1921.*
180 Stencil. *8¼x10⅝. Signed: Picasso 39/100. 1922.*
181 Stencil. *8¼x10½. Signed: Picasso 39/100. 1922.*
182 Stencil. *8⅜x10½. Signed: Picasso 39/100. 1922.*
183 Stencil. *10⅝x8½. Signed: Picasso 39/100. 1922.*
184 Stencil. *10⅜x8. Signed: Picasso 39/100. 1922.*
185 Stencil. *12⅜x8¼. Signed: Picasso 39/100. 1922.*
186 Stencil. *10½x8⅛. Signed: Picasso 39/100. 1922.*
187 Stencil. *11¼x8⅞. Signed: Picasso 39/100. 1922.*
188 Stencil. *10¾x8⅜. Signed: Picasso 39/100. 1922.*
189 Stencil. *11x8⅛. Signed: Picasso 39/100 1922. These ten stencils were published by Paul Rosenberg in Paris.*

## Renoir, Pierre Auguste.
*Born Limoges, France, 1841. Died Cagnes, France, 1919.*
190 The Bather. *Oil, 20¼ x 12. Signed: Renoir. 1918.*

### Rouault, Georges.
*Born Paris, 1871.*
191 Polichinelle. *Oil, 28½ x 20½. Unsigned. About 1931.*

### Rousseau, Henri (Le Douanier).
*Born Laval, France, 1844. Died Paris, 1910.*
192 Landscape with Cattle. *Oil, 20¼ x 26. Signed: Henri Julien Rousseau. 1895-1900.*
193 Merry Jesters (Joyeux Farceurs). *Oil, 57½ x 44½. Signed: Henri Julien Rousseau. 1906.*
194 Landscape. *Oil, 18 x 12⅞. Signed: H Rousseau. 1905-1910.*
195 Village Street Scene. *Oil, 16¼ x 13. Signed: Henri J Rousseau. Signed and dated on the back: Une vue de la route d'Auvers à Pontoise (Oise) H. Rousseau. Juillet 1909.*

### Roy, Pierre.
*Born Nantes, France, 1880.*
196 Metric System (Système Métrique). *Oil, 57½ x 38½. Signed: P. Roy. About 1930.*

### Schamberg, Morton.
*Born Philadelphia, 1881. Died Philadelphia, 1918. Lived in Paris from 1906 to 1909.*
197a Mechanical Abstraction. *Oil on board, 13¾ x 11. Signed and dated: Schamberg 1916.*
197b Landscape. *Oil on board, 13¾ x 11. Unsigned. 1916.*
    *The above (197a and 197b) are front and back of a single panel.*
198 Mechanical Abstraction. *Oil, 30 x 20. Signed and dated: Schamberg 1916.*

### Sheeler, Charles.
*Born Philadelphia, 1883.*
199 Barn Abstraction. *Black conté crayon, 14¼ x 19½. Signed and dated: Sheeler. 1917.*
    *Alternate title: Buck's County Barn.*
200 Barn Abstraction. *Black conté crayon and tempera, 17½ x 24. Signed and dated: Sheeler 1918.*
    *Alternate title: Buck's County Barn.*
201 Landscape. *Water color, 4¼ x 6⅝. Signed and dated: Sheeler 1925.*
202 Cactus. *Oil, 45 x 30. Signed and dated: Sheeler 1931.*

### Tanguy, Yves.
*Born Paris, 1900. Now lives in the United States.*
203 The Storm (L'Orage). *Oil, 32 x 25½. Signed and dated: Yves Tanguy 26. 1926.*
204 The Parallels. *Oil, 36¼ x 28¾. Signed and dated: Yves Tanguy 29. 1929.*

### Villon, Jacques.
*Born Damville, France, 1875.*
205 Sketch for Puteaux: Smoke and Trees in Bloom. No. 2 (Fumées et Arbres en Fleurs). *Oil, 18¼ x 21¼. Signed: Jacques Villon. 1912.*
206 Young Girl. *Oil, 57¾ x 45. Signed: Jacques Villon. 1912.*
    *Alternate title: Seated Figure of a Woman.*
207 Abstraction. *Oil, 22 x 26. Signed and dated: Jacques Villon 32. 1932.*

*Plates*

3: Jean Arp, *Constellation*

5: Constantin Brancusi, *The Kiss*

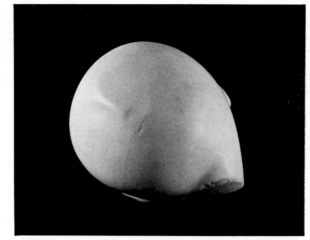

6: Constantin Brancusi, *Prometheus*

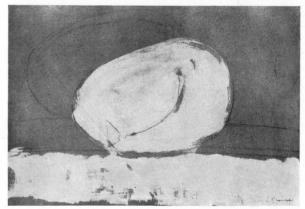

10: Constantin Brancusi, *Study for The New Born*

11: Constantin Brancusi, *The New Born*

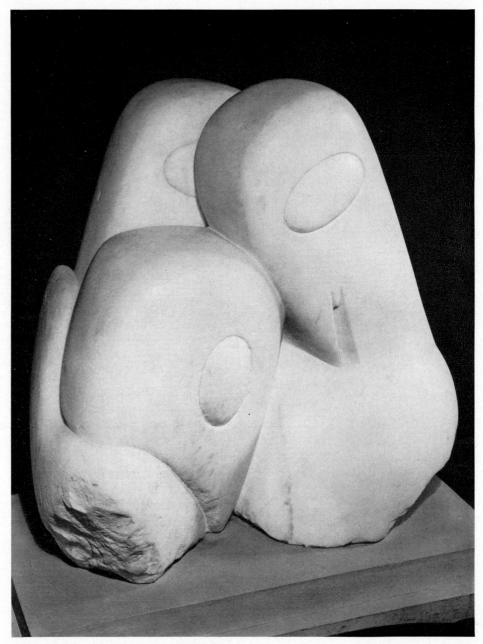

8: Constantin Brancusi, *Penguins*

13: Constantin Brancusi, *The Princess*

18: Constantin Brancusi, *The Fish*

14: Constantin Brancusi, *Chimera*

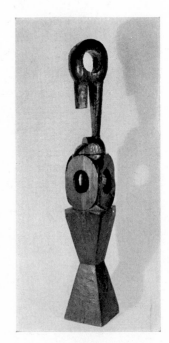

19: Constantin Brancusi, *Yellow Bird*

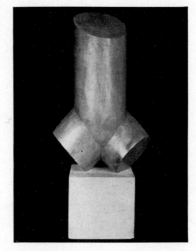

17: Constantin Brancusi, *Torso of a Young Man*

20: Constantin Brancusi, *Sculpture for the Blind*

30:  Georges Braque, *Musical Forms*

31a:  Georges Braque, *Still Life*

31b: Georges Braque, *The Table*

26: Georges Braque, *Still Life (with the word Vin)*    27: Georges Braque, *Still Life (oval)*

32: Georges Braque, *Violin and Pipe*

36: Paul Cézanne, *Still Life with Apples*

35: Alexander Calder, *Mobile*

40: Marc Chagall, *Half-Past Three*

41: Giorgio de Chirico, *The Soothsayer's Recompense*

45: Salvador Dali, *Soft Construction with Boiled Beans; Premonition of Civil War*

46: Robert Delaunay, *St. Severin*       51: André Derain, *Woman*

53:  Marcel Duchamp, *The Artist's Father*          56:  Marcel Duchamp, *The Sonata*

57 : Marcel Duchamp, *Yvonne and Magdeleine Torn in Tatters*

58: Marcel Duchamp, *Portrait*

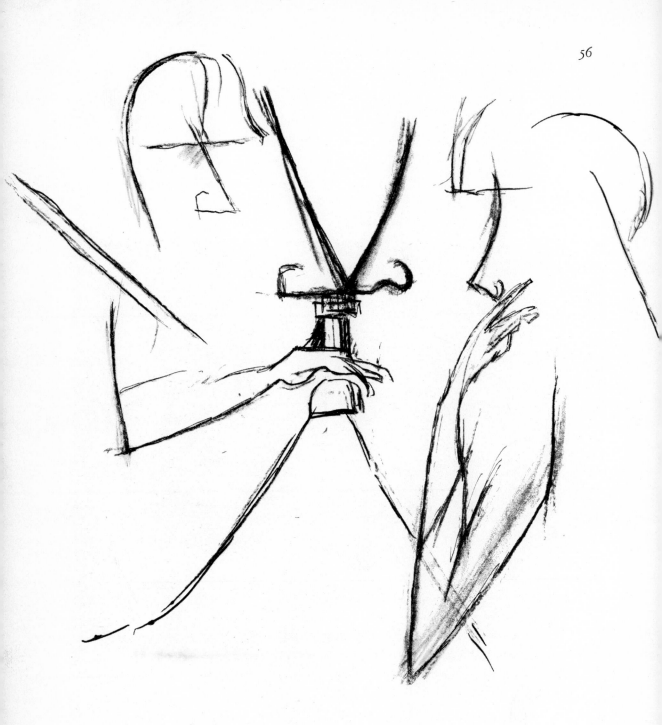

59: Marcel Duchamp, *Study for The Chess Players*

60: Marcel Duchamp, *The Chess Players*

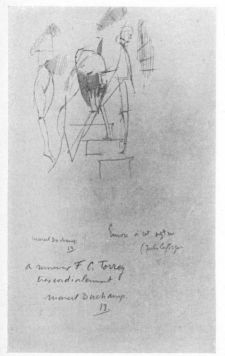

61                                                                      62

61:  Marcel Duchamp, *Study for Nude Descending a Staircase*

62:  Marcel Duchamp, *Nude Descending a Staircase, Number 1*

64:  Marcel Duchamp, *Nude Descending a Staircase, Number 3*

63:  Marcel Duchamp, *Nude Descending a Stai*

*mber 2*

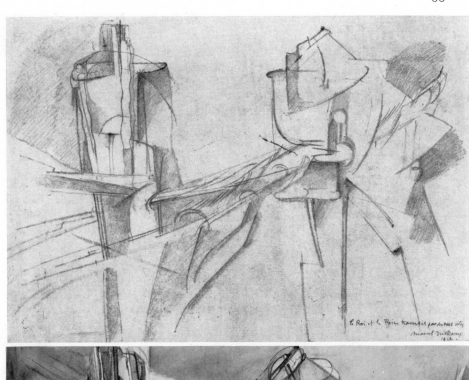

67: Marcel Duchamp, *The King and Queen Surrounded by Swift Nudes*

65: Marcel Duchamp, *Study for The King and Queen (upper left)*

66: Marcel Duchamp, *Study for The King and Queen (lower left)*

68: Marcel Duchamp, *Study for The Virgin*

69: Marcel Duchamp, *The Bride*

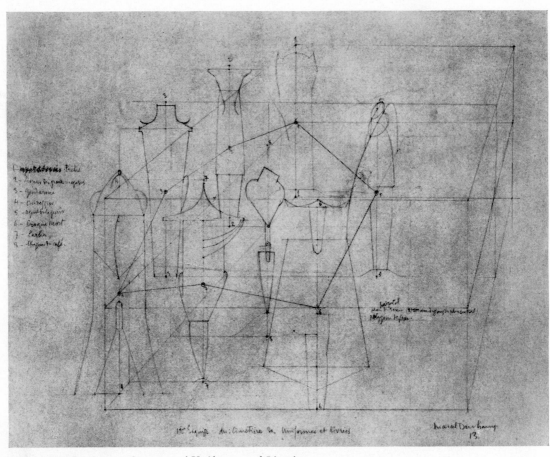

70:  Marcel Duchamp, *Cemetery of Uniforms and Liveries*

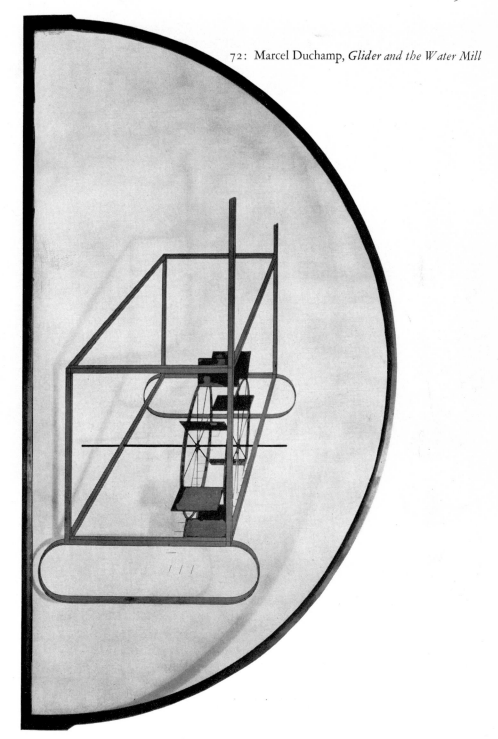

72: Marcel Duchamp, *Glider and the Water Mill*

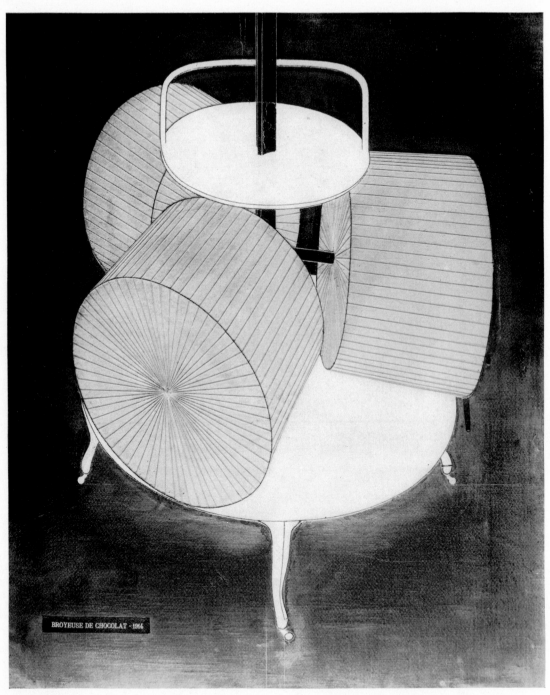

BROYEUSE DE CHOCOLAT - 1914

74: Marcel Duchamp, *Chocolate Grinder, Number 2*

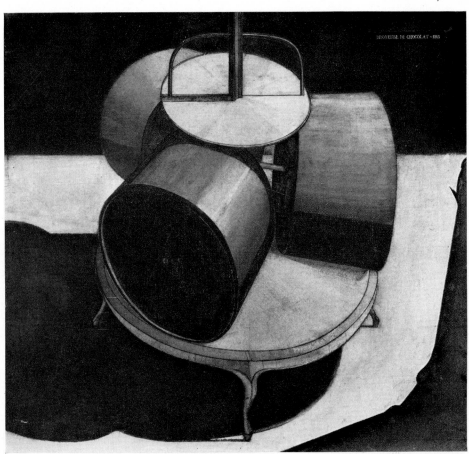

73: Marcel Duchamp, *Chocolate Grinder, Number 1*

77: Marcel Duchamp, *Ready-made, Girl with Bedstead*

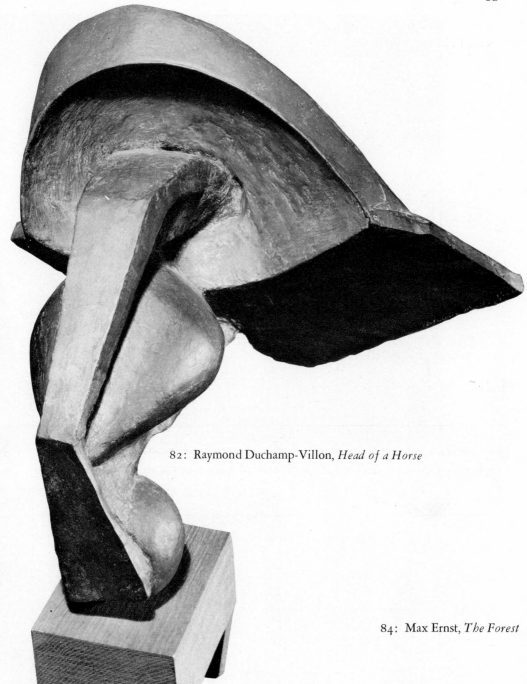

82: Raymond Duchamp-Villon, *Head of a Horse*

84: Max Ernst, *The Forest*

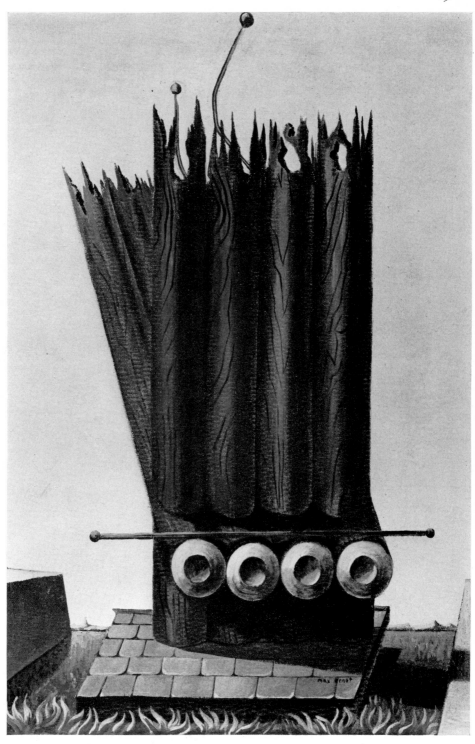

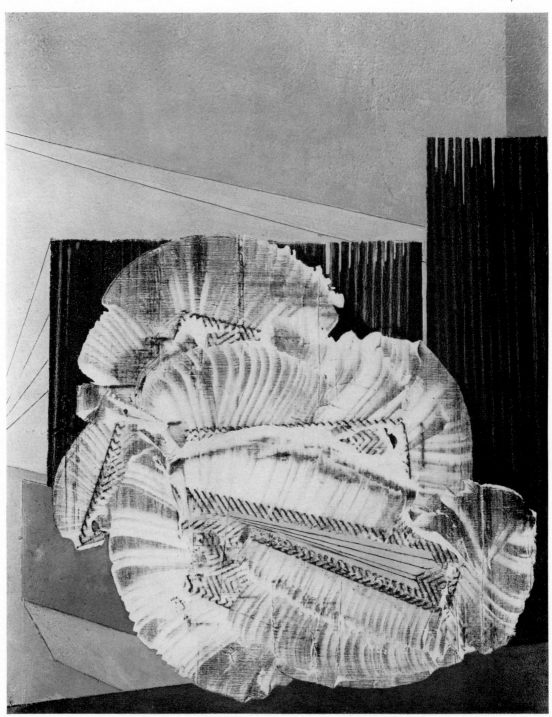

85: Max Ernst, *Flower*

88: Roger de la Fresnaye, *Nude*    92: Albert Gleizes, *Woman at the Piano*

93: Juan Gris, *The Man in the Café*  94: *(right)* Juan Gris, *La Place Ravignan*

95: Juan Gris, *The Lamp*

98: *(above)* Jean Hélion, *Red Tensions*  103: *(below)* Wassily Kandinsky, *Improvisation*

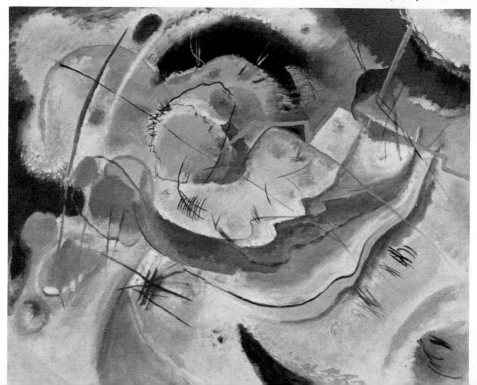

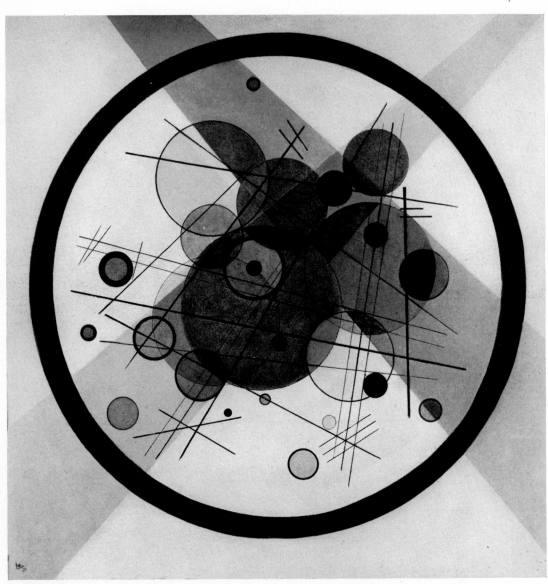

104: Wassily Kandinsky, *Circles in Circle*

107: Wassily Kandinsky, *Fish Form*

105: Wassily Kandinsky, *Landscape*

108: Wassily Kandinsky, *Isolated Objects*

117:  Paul Klee, *Fish Magic*

111: *(above)* Paul Klee, *Goldfish Wife*　　　　116: *(below)* Paul Klee, *Jörg*

120: Paul Klee, *Village Carnival*

123: Paul Klee, *Prestidigitator*

121: Paul Klee, *Journey in Corsica*

128: Frank Kupka, *Fugue in Two Colors*

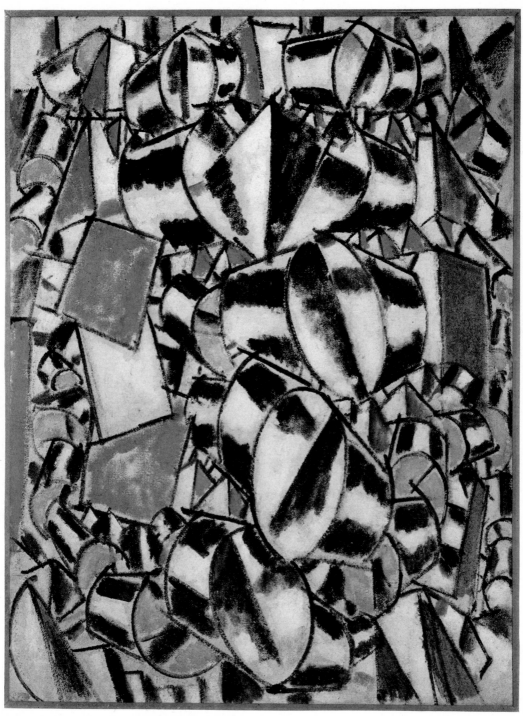

130:  Fernand Léger, *Contrast of Forms*

131: Fernand Léger, *The City*

134: René Magritte, *The Six Elements*

136: André Masson, *Animal Caught in a Trap*

137: Henri Matisse, *Mlle. Yvonne Landsberg*

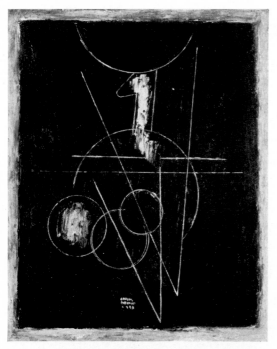

141: Carlos Mérida, *Deer Dance*

142: Knud Merrild, *Portrait of D. H. Lawrence*

145: Jean Metzinger, *Tea Time*

149:  Joan Miró, *Nude*

152: Joan Miró, *Figure*

154: Joan Miró, *The Lovers*

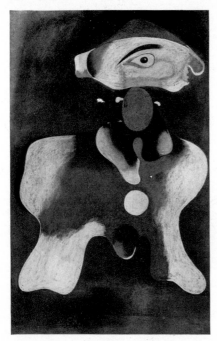

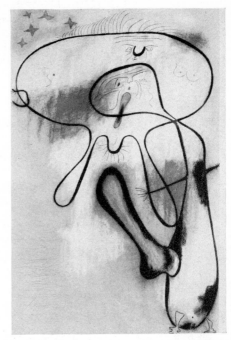

155: Joan Miró, *Person in the Presence of Nature*

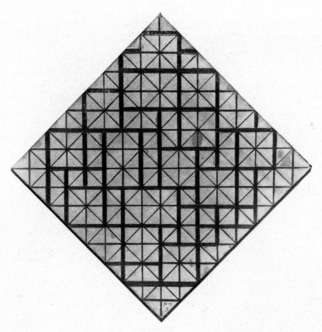

157: Piet Mondrian, *Composition in Black and Gray*

158: Piet Mondrian, *Composition*

160:  Francis Picabia, *Dances at the Spring*

162: Francis Picabia, *Physical Culture*

163: Pablo Picasso, *Old Woman*

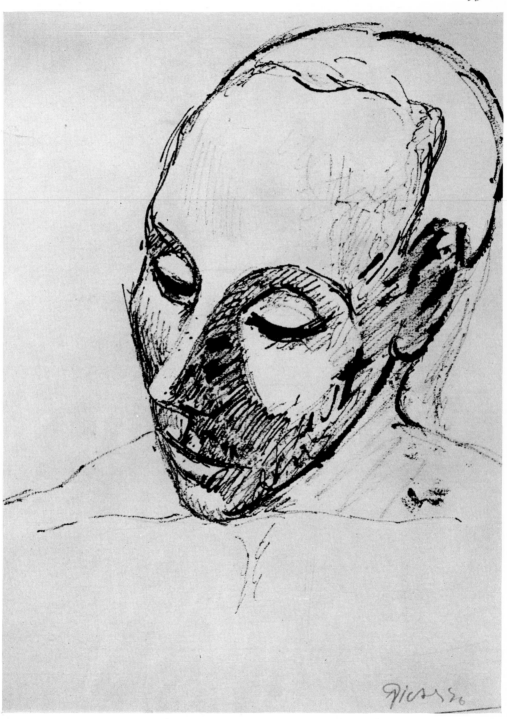

166: Pablo Picasso, *Head*

167: Pablo Picasso, *Woman Seated and Woman Standing*

169: Pablo Picasso, *Seated Nude Woman*

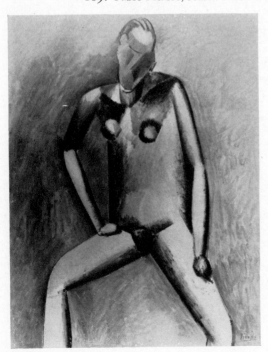

172: Pablo Picasso, *Female Nude*

173: Pablo Picasso, *Violin*

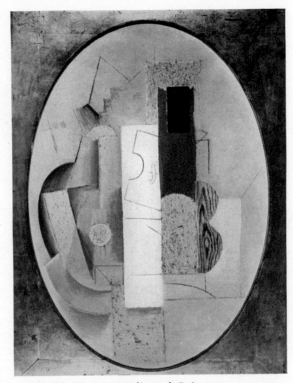

177: Pablo Picasso, *Violin and Guitar*

174: Pablo Picasso, *Man with Violin*

178: Pablo Picasso, *Three Nudes on Shore*

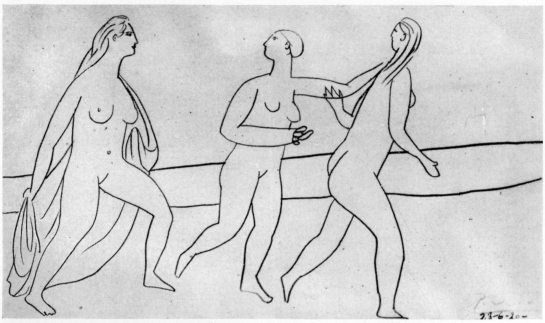

179: Pablo Picasso, *Still Life*

191: Georges Rouault, *Polichinelle*

193:  Henri Rousseau, *Merry Jesters*

192: Henri Rousseau, *Landscape with Cattle*

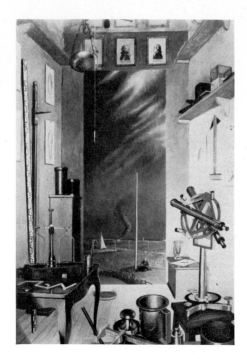

196: Pierre Roy, *Metric System*

203: Yves Tanguy, *The Storm*

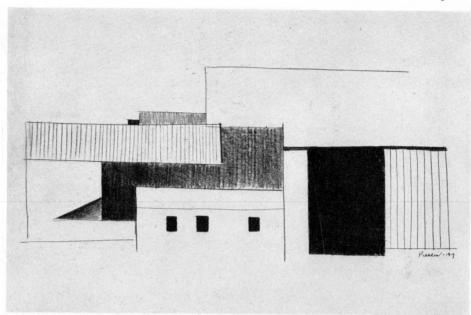

199: *(above)* Charles Sheeler, *Barn Abstraction*   207: *(below)* Jacques Villon, *Abstraction*

206: Jacques Villon, *Young Girl*